THE LAST KIDS ON EARTH

THRILLING TALES FROM THE TREE HOUSE

Written by **MAX BRALLIER**

With illustrations by **DOUGLAS HOLGATE,**
Lorena Alvarez Gómez, Xavier Bonet,
Jay Cooper, Christopher Mitten,
and Anoosha Syed

SCHOLASTIC INC.

No part of this publication may be reproduced, stored in a retrieval system, or transmitted in any form or by any means, electronic, mechanical, photocopying, recording, or otherwise, without written permission of the publisher. For information regarding permission, write to Viking Children's Books, an imprint of Penguin Young Readers Group, a division of Penguin Random House LLC, Permissions Department, 1745 Broadway, 15th Floor, New York, NY 10019.

ISBN 978-1-338-79134-1

12 11 10 9 8 7 6 5 4 3 2 1   21 22 23 24 25 26

Printed in the U.S.A.   44

First Scholastic printing, September 2021

Book design by Jim Hoover
Set in Cosmiqua Com and Carrotflower

LOOK UPON MY AMBIENT MOOD LIGHTING AND DESPAIR.

For Alyse.   —M. B.

To the Grundy Outlaws: Angus, Syd,
Noah, Jak, Jake, Flynn, and Hamish.
Do it for Silverwings. Do it for Phil,
and do it for the gang!   —D. H.

CONTENTS

SWINGIN' JACK SULLIVAN
& THE GOOD NEWS BUDDIES IN . . .
DANGER ON THE DIAMOND!

BOOM! GRAND SLAM! It's a walk-off, it's a walk-off. . . .

Another game of Sgt. Baseball's Home Run Slaughter—and another victory for Team Quack. QUACK! QUACK!

Your team name is dumb.

That was bunk! I had the sun in my eyes!

story by **Max Brallier**   art by **Xavier Bonet**

Whoa, the sun's up?

Have we been playing all night?

It is easy to lose track of time during the apocalypse, friend . . .

Sonic screwdrivers— that **reminds** me! Guys! You know what today is?

JUMP!

MONSTERS BEHAVING HORRIBLY MONTAGE!

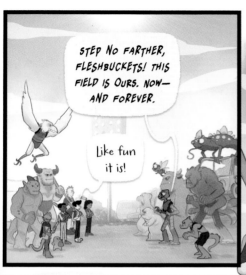

STEP NO FARTHER, FLESHBUCKETS! THIS FIELD IS OURS. NOW— AND FOREVER.

Like fun it is!

CAREFUL, HUMANS. THAT'S BURKIN—AND THESE ARE THE STONEBURGERS. A BAND OF GRUMPS.

I eat bands of grumps for breakfast. . . .

You eat Teddy Grahams for breakfast, Jack. And like I told you, **that's** why you're so tired in the afternoon.

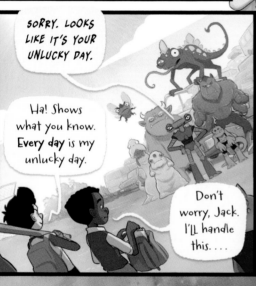

SORRY. LOOKS LIKE IT'S YOUR UNLUCKY DAY.

Ha! Shows what you know. **Every day** is my unlucky day.

Don't worry, Jack. I'll handle this. . . .

I'm afraid you're the one who's out of luck, Burkin. Field usage requests must be filed forty-eight hours in advance, in person, at the Wakefield Parks and Community Services Center. Now, I sure hope you filed the proper paperwork . . . or, oh boy, are you gonna look silly.

Only you can make a fight like this uncool.

BEEEEEEEELLLLCH!

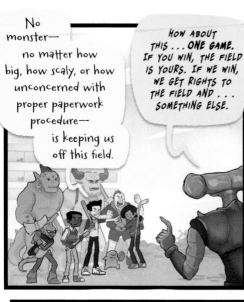

No monster— no matter how big, how scaly, or how unconcerned with proper paperwork procedure— is keeping us off this field.

HOW ABOUT THIS... ONE GAME. IF YOU WIN, THE FIELD IS YOURS. IF WE WIN, WE GET RIGHTS TO THE FIELD AND... SOMETHING ELSE.

Sure! Fine! Whatever it is, we're in!

Personally, I'd love to know what the "something else" is before we start agreeing to things.

Of course. Otherwise—

NOPE! DOESN'T MATTER! WHATEVER IT IS, WE'RE PLAYING. Deal?

DEAL.

Well, Jack— now that it's too late to do anything about it—I would love to know what we're playing for.

Fine, fine.

WHISPER, WHISPER

What?! ... OUR SOULS?!?

TOMORROW. DAWN.

THE NEXT DAY. DAWN.
CRACK!
FIZZZ
GULP!
Listen up, team!
CRUNCH!
What are we gonna do?
NOT LOSE!
When are we gonna do it?
IN A FEW MINUTES!
Because when the going gets tough, the tough get going!
Which is a phrase that confuses me because "get going" means "leave" and leaving when things get tough doesn't sound very tough at all, but whatever, you get the gist!
Now, let's go out there and **show these bad guys who's who!!**
I WISH JUNE WAS COACH.
Sing it, sister.

I'll confirm, but yes, I believe we are using *Rock N' Jock* scoring.

GLOBLET! You're coaching our rivals?!

What?? How could you??

They told me I had a cool hat.

We're in a fight, Globs.

Again?

OK, everyone. It's time . . . LET'S PLAY SOME BALL!

Well, this is **not** going like I'd hoped. . . .

PTUI!

WOO-HOO, TWENTY-SEVEN TASTY POINTS!

I AM SPLITTING THESE DULL, ROUND CREATURES OPEN AT AN EXTRAORDINARY RATE!

SLASHUU!!

SKREEEEEE!!!

Charge the mound, buddy!

I will not.

Enough! Time! TIME-OUT!

15

Deal's off! This isn't baseball!

This *is* baseball. At least the way it's played in our dimension.

You sound like Johnny Steve . . . !

Gosh, I miss that owl-shaped bum.

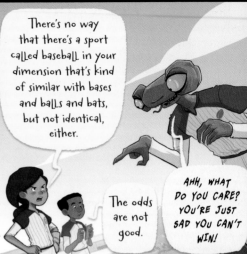

There's no way that there's a sport called baseball in your dimension that's kind of similar with bases and balls and bats, but not identical, either.

The odds are not good.

AHH, WHAT DO YOU CARE? YOU'RE JUST SAD YOU CAN'T WIN!

Fine! We'll play your way and we'll WIN. Come on, guys. . . .

POW!

SLIDE!

This should tie it up!

SLAM!

Ugh...

Bardle? What...?

YOU PLAY FOR THE HONOR OF JOE'S PIZZA, JACK. AND YOUR ENEMIES?

WHO DO THEY PLAY FOR?

What?

Bardle, stop talking in riddles just once! You're dreamworld Bardle—just give it to me straight!

SIGH.

FINE, JACK. THE STONEBURG MONSTERS' UNIFORMS. THINK ABOUT THEIR UNIFORMS!

Their uniforms...?

Herman's Hot Dog Palace Bonanza-Rama!

I have come to claim my friend.

Well, more June's friend, really. I mean, we're **all** friends.

But Globlet and I don't hang out one-on-one much.

I just kinda think we wouldn't have that much to talk about.

But then again, maybe we would! And maybe we should hang out more! Am I just being . . .

HEEEEEEY, BEASTIE BEASTIE! SUH-WIIIING, BEASTIE!

WE NEED A PITCHER, NOT A BELLY ITCHER!

Give us back Globlet, why you gotta **hog** her!

NOW!

GRUNT

RAWR!

DUCK!

JUNE! I knew you would come for me!

Oh, hi, Jack.

Did you hear what I was saying? Do you think we should hang out more?

I'm good.

WALL CRUMBLE!

He didn't even use a gadget. . . .

27

END!

Oohmygosh, Chef, you'll NEVER guess the dream I had!

Siiigh...

COURSE NOT. IT WAS YOUR DREAM, GLOB—

See, I was THE most important monster in the globosphere, and I could do **anything** I wanted, and everyone loved me. Even you! Well, everyone except . . .

MAYO!

YOU DONE SCOLDING THE MAYO? 'CAUSE WE GOT COOKIN' TO DO.

What's on the menu today, Cheffy Pants?

We meet again. . . . I told you, stay out of my dreams!

Tie!!

2 HOT 2 HANDLE

YOU, LITTLE GOO WAD, ARE ABOUT TO FIND OUT WHY *INTERDIMENSIONAL MICHELIN MAGAZINE* AWARDED ME *ZERO* GOLDEN TIRES. WE'RE MAKING THE ULTIMATE POWER SUB!

FWAP!!

I'M GONNA NEED A METRIC TON OF SHREDDED MOZZ, EXACTLY TWENTY-SEVEN FEET OF LICORICE, AAAAAND A JAR OF SAP FROM THE OL' MAPLE TREE OUT BACK.

Joe's NRG BOOSTER SUB!

31

TENSE KNIFE FLIP!

SLOW-MO STYLE!

SLIIICE!

THUNK!

UH-OH!

uh-oh.

AAHHHHH!!

AAHHH!!

Bubble

Bubble

SHAAKE

SHAAAKE

POP!

POP!

Um.

POP!

GEEZ, GLOB, DID YOU KNOW YOU COULD DO THAT?

Oh yeah yeah, tooooootally... NOT!

33

Meanwhile, at the tree house . . .

1st ANNUAL FOOD MASTER FRENZY

Thirty seconds! Jack, you'd better start plating . . .

My cherry glaze isn't ready!!

TIME'S UP!!

Utensils DOWN!

RRRIIING!!!

NO EXCUSES!

I had to ice this whole cake with one lousy piping bag.

Meep! Sigh. Yeep!

OK, Rover. Winner gets a full week off of dish duty.

So choose carefully.

I swear, if my Butterfinger buttercream isn't enough to take first place . . .

bite bite!

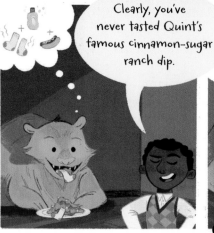

Clearly, you've never tasted Quint's famous cinnamon-sugar ranch dip.

I can't watch! Tell me when it's over!

39

Stay away from my BFF, ya hear?

POKE!

hop!

If she's **your** BFF, she's **my** BFF. I AM you.

NO! June and I went on a wild flight and a cool guy wrote a book about it, and *you* weren't there, and *I* was, and we had the BEST time, and you wouldn't know **anything** about it!

Ouch!

Oh, *wouldn't I*? Tell me, how *are* Neon and Johnny Steve these days?

<Gasp!> You *MONSTER*.

OK settle down, Globlet. Or, wait . . .

Shoot, it's hard to tell you guys apart!

June, ol' buddy, ol' pal! It's *me*! Your BFF! WHAT CAN I DO TO PROVE IT??

Relax, Globlet. I believe you.

Oh, June. *Tsk tsk.* You just made a **globumental** mistake.

frosting

linglob memorial

glob-sphinx

statue of globerty

glob he

10000
IN GLOB
10000

Globa l

mount globmore !!

globfel tower ♥

glob day parade ☺

Wait ... WHAT? This is a Glob-Off? THIS??

You think you can take me, hot shot?

That's right. I am a hot shot. And you're a not-shot!

Wooooow. Good one.

Three hours later ...

How much longer?? This is worse than Jack and Quint's weekend-long *Galaxy Quest* marathon.

Hey! *Galaxy Quest* is a quality film with limitless review value. It should be watched daily, at minimum!

More like ad nauseum.

GASP!

DROP!!

NO!

AAAAHHHHHHHHHHHH!!!

Stretch—

GASP!

Wicked.

gulp!

Ah-choo!!

CLANK!

Oops! My bad.

Globlet! Globlet! Globlet! Globlet! Globlet!

Globlet, buddy, you did it!!

Go, my children!

Be free.

Frolic into the night!

Order the most expensive sushi on the menu!

DANCE LIKE NOBODY'S WATCHING! BE THE GLOB YOU WISH TO SEE IN THE WORLD.

END!

THE PERNICIOUS PUTTY PREDICAMENT

Story by ~~Max Brallier~~ art by ~~Jay Cooper~~

Story and Art by Quint BAKER

We find our heroes at home, assuming their everyday, non-hero alter egos: **Quint Baker** and **Jack Sullivan**. Mild-mannered best friends, and two of the last kids on Earth. Just another day at the tree house at the end of the world ...

Quint, I am having the **WORST DAY!**

Uh-huh ...

JOE'S PIZZA

And I'm feeling **extra whiny** about it!

That's no good.

First, I didn't get to sleep in late because the sun was being, like, **EXTRA SUNNY!**

Then **ALL THE DONUTS WERE GONE.** So, I had to eat toast. **TOAST.** It's just **HARD BREAD!**

Then Rover yanked out the power cord before I could save my game! It's just been a really bad day and—

Bad day! Did you say "bad day"? Well, that, Jack, is something I can solve.

No, no. You don't need to solve it. I really just wanted to—

SOLVE IT! I know, I was listening.

Lucky for you, I just completed the world's first scientific cure for "the bad day"!

CUE THE ADVERTISEMENT!

*QUINT NOTE: Technically, the patent is still pending.
But only because the patent office is currently overrun by very inventive zombies!

63

64

65

The Mobile-Pong Ping-Pong Ramp-Pong!

Unbelievable. ALL of my inventions, turning on their creator: ME! It's like I'm being confronted by my worst nightmare!

Wait a second. I thought your worst nightmare was—

UPLOADING... UPLOADING... UPLOADING...

Sitting down for video game time only to discover you have to install a 549-GB, 19-hour update! Or ...

Accidentally making a peanut butter and jellyFISH sammich! Or ...

Putting your socks on AFTER your shoes. Again.

SCHOOL

70

WORSE THINGS WE'VE FACED BEFORE!

The time Jack messed up and unleashed the Popcorn Virus from Venus!

Soooo buttery.

Or the time Jack left the faucet running and released the Terrible Bath Trolls of Southern Hades!

Hold still! I'm trying to clean behind your ears!

Or the time Jack thought my nuclear-waste bin was the microwave and created Meltdown Mozzarella: The Atomic Pizza! With all the toppings!

Oooh! There's glowing cheese in the crust!

Well then, guess we better save the day.

SUPER DJ BUMP

Guess so, friend.

Quickly, to the Loveable-Genius-Mobile and the Sidekick-Spring-Along!

72

73

75

Sometimes, when you've got big emotions, you just need to **talk** about them. And you need someone to **listen**. Science is no substitute for sharing how we feel with the people who care most:

79

So, why're these Rifters attackin' you, anyway?

On account of us having the only working Sugar-Slurp machine in these parts. They're trying to steal it, and that ain't right.

Meeks—he's the Rifters' leader. He craves that sweet, sugary nectar. His whole band of Rifters are big-time sugar heads. But that Sugar-Slurp machine is ours! We found it and fixed it up real good!

Wyther has a plan for the Sugar-Slurp.

Our whole band will start makin' our way west, stopping at outposts, settlements, and the like. Make an honest living selling the frozen goodness.

Grumble...

What's 'a matter?

You don't like frozen sugar drinks?

Nah, not that.

I don't like being lost. And that, right now, is what we are.

90

Here we are. Home sweet home. The Rifters don't usually attack until nightfall.

WELL, let's giddyup then. Daylight's burnin'.

HAVE YOU BROUGHT THE EYE, EEWEE? THE SOONER I CAN GET BACK TO HEALTH, THE SOONER WE CAN END THIS....

Yes, great one. I have retrieved it.

AND WHO'S THIS?

99

KA-BOOM!

SEED SHRAPNEL!

END!

SWISH!

My bad!

YES. TOO FAR.

TRY AGAIN, HUMAN JUNE.

ARF?

FASTER, FOUR LEGS! WE WILL BLAST IT FROM THE SKY!

THROW!

GRUNT

FLY, CLAUDIA! FLY FAST AND STRIKE FATAL!

MISS!

FAIL!

OH DARN.

APPLE

FLARFGH!
KER-KRASH!

107

Rover! You OK?

DO YOU SEE HER? WHERE IS MY CLAUDIA?!

Oh... Oh wow.

<Sniff!>

That smell.

WHAT... WHAT....IS THIS PLACE, JUNE?

THIS LOOKS TO BE THE LARGEST CELEBRATION OF A HUMAN CHILD'S DELIVERY DAY I HAVE EVER SET EYES UPON.

Huh, what? No, Skaelka—it's a carnival.

Wakefield's official summer kickoff. My parents took me every year.

Everything must've just stopped. Right when, y'know, everything else started.

WHAT IS THAT TREMENDOUS SCENT?

<INHALE!>

Kettle corn.

And it's not a tremendous scent.

It's the worst odor ever.

Hey— YIKES! Clown Zombie.

WHAT KIND OF WEIRD HUMAN-CARNIVAL THING IS THIS?

IT IS FUN TO SIT ABOVE A BOX OF LIQUID?

No, no. The fun is for us. Not the one sitting.

GLURGH.

Watch ...

FLING!

TING!

AHH, THE OL' PLUNGE-THE-TRAITOR-INTO-THE-ACID-VAT GAME!

MER?

KER-SPLASH!

WE HAVE THAT IN MY DIMENSION, THOUGH IT IS MUCH MORE FUN. THEIR TRAITOROUS SCREAMS REALLY TICKLE THE FUNNY BONES.

Wait. Something's **weird** about this guy, though.

HUMAN JUNE...

WHAT IS IT?

Something I...can't quite...

GRB-GRB-GRB...

Whoa. Wouldja look at that!

BLEGKT! BLEG!

BLEGKT!

113

SCOOCH OVER. THIS SEAT IS TOO SMALL FOR MY MUSCLES.

Ow, hey. Your spikes are pokin' me.

RAWLF!

HA-HA! THOSE BEASTS ARE BOGUS!

BUT THESE ONES ARE REAL! MUCH MORE SATISFYING!

Skaelka, no! We don't destroy zombies!

Those zombies were once in someone's family. We have to be careful.

WHAT'S THAT, CLAUDIA? JUNE RUINS ALL THE FUN? YES, YES, I AGREE.

Skaelka, I know the axe doesn't talk.

Something's up with these zombies. They're **different**.

And we need to find out **why**.

We gotta get a closer look at those slug things. They're making these zombies act **extra dangerous**.

119

The last time I was here, I was eight years old. And I overdid it. Big-time. Fried EVERYTHING. Fried dough, fried Oreos, fried pickles on a stick, fried pickles not on a stick. And I topped it all off with five bags of the freshest, saltiest kettle corn that ever existed....

I felt sick, but I got on the Gravity-Spinster anyway....

I refused to miss out....

And halfway through the ride, I—

EJECTED THE PARTIALLY DIGESTED FOOD-STUFF UPWARD THROUGH YOUR MOUTH HOLE.

Oh! No! My clothes!

Someone stop the ride!

It's in my hair!

It's in my ear!

It's in my ear hair!

JUNE, THAT STORY WAS TRULY REVOLTING. AND GLORIOUS.

THANK YOU FOR SHARING.

I'm happy it made you happy.

But it was just about the most embarrassing thing that—

RECORD SCRATCH!

Hold the landline! It's time for our story!

EVIE SNARK & GHAZT THE GENERAL IN...

THE EPIC TALE OF EPIC STUFF YOU NEVER SAW HAPPEN (BUT SHOULD PROBABLY KNOW ABOUT!)

THIS TALE WILL EXPLAIN PERTINENT EVENTS BETWEEN BOOKS FOUR AND SEVEN.

story by
Max Brallier

art by Douglas Holgate

And then I struck pay dirt.

BOOM BANG

BOOM! BOOM! BANG

Sorta . . .

WHOA!

BAM!

SKREEEE!

SLICE!

SKEE-ARRR!

Come on! I dare ya!

HISSSS

MISS!

SWIPE!

151

I went searching for my ball. It had landed in a monster's empty eye socket.

The lump heaved as the Cosmic Servant fed—sucking the dead monster's guts like a breakfast smoothie. I watched the vines jerk and snap.

The ball bobbed as the wet lump convulsed.

And that image—it reminded me of something . . .

I had photocopied a few of the most important pages from *Interdimensional Terrors: A History of the Cabal of the Cosmic.*

ZIP

Where were those pages . . . Not the Conjuration of Agony. No, not Painful Resurrection. Not Suffering Locusts.

Where was—

YES! Brutish Transmutify! Exactly as I remember it.

It was suddenly clear what I had to do—as clear as Wonder Woman's jet. And if it worked, I would never be anybody's servant again . . .

*AUTHOR'S NOTE: See *The Last Kids on Earth and the Cosmic Beyond.* Jack steals the book! It's a big deal!

The next day, when I returned—I was happy. I had the makings of a plan.

♪ ♫ ♪ Evie Snark, Evie Snark, does whatever... ♫ ♪

And on that same happy day, at long last, the Servant awoke.

HEY! FINALLY!

GROAN...

Good morning, sleepyhead!

The servant, Thrull, started talking, and I learned that Ghazt hadn't told me everything. In fact, he hadn't told me much of anything. He had left out the most important part... THE TOWER.

That was the final straw. It was a good thing I had the makings of a plan—because now, I was going to put it into play—without question...

!! FUME SHAKE

IF THE TAIL IS THE KEY TO GHAZT BUILDING HIS ARMY AND CONSTRUCTING THE TOWER, I WILL HELP YOU RETRIEVE IT. FOR GHAZT. FOR BEZZOCH.

BUT FIRST, WE MUST DEAL WITH THESE LITTLE HUMANS. . . .

I couldn't believe what my eyes were seeing.

No . . .

Duped and deceived! By a double-crossing cosmic crumb bun!

Thrull would destroy Jack and his friends next. I didn't want to stay and watch. So I left . . .

I walked for hours. Rain came in buckets. I was glad for it—the way the outside world perfectly matched what I felt on the inside . . .

159

I raced through the streets. Leaving Ghazt had me feeling revitalized, rejuvenated. Because I knew I wouldn't be anyone's servant again.

I would rise on my own.

I returned to the ABC theater. The place where all my big plans went wrong. Where Meathook fell.

Meathook had been powerful. We had been a good team.

SUCH A GOOD TEAM!

He handled the four little fools.

But then he was buried beneath two tons of broken movie theater balcony.

Ghazt had arrived. Ghazt was the future. So, I left Meathook behind.

That was a jerk move, for sure. He had served me well. But I'd no longer had any need for him.

But I could make it up to him. By letting him serve me once again . . .

Ooh, Milk Duds.

CRUNCH!
CLINK, CLINK . . .

Uh?

Something BIG was alive in the ABC Cinema . . . I hoped it was him . . .

My heart pounded as I entered the theater—the place my life should have changed for the better. Instead of the opposite...

MURRRMMMM...
RAWRRRRNNN...

My heart vaulted into my throat.

Meathook! I'm coming!

Need a lever...

STAB!

Stupid... super-heavy...

fancy... recline... seats...!

163

*AUTHOR'S NOTE: That's Quint's fault! See *The Last Kids on Earth and the Cosmic Beyond.*

It was time to feed the concoction to my monstrous friend. And the sweet self-serve soda machine would be my delivery system . . .

I felt like Link as I poured each ingredient into a different tube.

Double, double, toil and trouble. Bubble, bubble, Barnie Rubble!

Later . . .

Hey, Meathook! You're awake! Right on! If you had weird dreams about a bunch of tubes being hooked up to you—well, those weren't dreams.

You are going to love this. Each ingredient is connected to a different tube. And they all flow directly into you.

Soon, you'll be more than just a monstrous punching machine. You'll be **my** monstrous punching machine.

Now, how do you feel about a little hint of cherry vanilla? I'm a cherry vanilla gal, myself.

WELL, WELL, WELL. LOOK WHO HAS RETURNED.

I HAVE RECOVERED. AND I AM STRONGER THAN EVER.

IT IS TIME I GET BACK MY TAIL, MY POWER SOURCE. I SHALL CRUSH THAT THRULL CRETIN FOR CROSSING ME.

Wow, I leave for a few days and you get your mojo back!

Anger has you focused up, huh?

Or wait. Is it something else...?

You're scared! That's it. You're afraid! Because... because if Thrull builds the Tower, then Rezzóch will come.

And he'll be super angry at you! Because Thrull will have done what you failed to do.

YOU SEE MORE THAN I REALIZED.

TAP TAP TAP

What can I say? Thick lenses.

Days later . . .

WE GO THROUGH THAT.

An old highway tunnel? Great, you know how I love being underground . . .

You know—you need to figure out a way for your brain GPS to take us on less dangerous paths.

TAP TAP

MY BRAIN NAVIGATION IS SUPERIOR. DO NOT DISRESPECT IT.

CLICK!

TRIP!

SPIKE SPIRAL!

That's not gonna be good . . .

So, what is this thing?

A Mælûsqçât. The largest creature I've ever encountered!

SNIIFF SNIFF

GASP!

MMMM... I'LL BE INSIDE.

SNIFF SNIFF SNIFF SNIFF SNIFF

FLOAT!

Tell me—is there any way to direct the creature?

Not really... It appears impossible to control this great beast.

However, it does seem to sense when a monster is in great pain...

Acknowledgments

THIS BOOK WAS a team effort—more than any other Last Kids book—and I'm thankful to so many people. Douglas Holgate—the man with the million-dollar hips (again). Dana Leydig, for endless help and guidance. Jim Hoover, for seeing this thing, getting it, understanding it, and guiding it. Leila Sales, for jumping in at the last minute. All the incredible illustrators who made this work: Lorena Alvarez Gómez, Xavier Bonet, Jay Cooper, Christopher Mitten, and Anoosha Syed. Josh Pruett, for so much. Jennifer Dee, for making so much happen during a time when making things happened seemed impossible. And my endless thanks to Abigail Powers, Janet B. Pascal, Krista Ahlberg, Marinda Valenti, Emily Romero, Elyse Marshall, Carmela Iaria, Christina Colangelo, Felicity Vallence, Sarah Moses, Kara Brammer, Alex Garber, Lauren Festa, Michael Hetrick, Kim Ryan, Helen Boomer, and everyone in PYR Sales and PYR Audio. Ken Wright, more than ever. Dan Lazar, Cecilia de la Campa, Torie Doherty-Munro, and everyone at Writers House.

MAX BRALLIER!

is a *New York Times*, *USA Today*, and *Wall Street Journal* bestselling author. His books and series include The Last Kids on Earth, Eerie Elementary, Mister Shivers, Can YOU Survive the Zombie Apocalypse?, and Galactic Hot Dogs. He is a writer and producer for Netflix's Emmy-award-winning adaptation of The Last Kids on Earth. Max lives in Los Angeles with his wife and daughter.

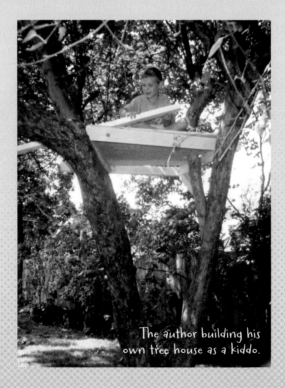

The author building his own tree house as a kiddo.

DOUGLAS HOLGATE!

is the illustrator of the *New York Times* bestselling series, The Last Kids on Earth from Penguin Young Readers (now also an Emmy-winning Netflix animated series) and the co-creator and illustrator of the graphic novel *Clem Hetherington and the Ironwood Race* for Scholastic Graphix.

He has worked for the last twenty years making books and comics for publishers around the world from his garage in Melbourne, Australia. He lives with his family (and a large fat dog that could possibly be part polar bear) in the Australian bush on five acres surrounded by eighty-million-year-old volcanic boulders.

Big Mama visited the Penguin offices once.

Lorena Alvarez Gómez was born and raised in Bogotá, and studied graphic design and arts at the Universidad Nacional de Colombia. She has illustrated for children's books, independent publications, advertising, and fashion magazines.

Xavier Bonet is an illustrator and a comic book artist who lives in Barcelona with his wife and two children. He has illustrated a number of middle grade books, including two in the Thrifty Guide series by Jonathan Stokes and Michael Dahl's Really Scary Stories series. He loves all things retro, video games, and Japanese food, but above all, spending time with his family.

Jay Cooper is a graphic designer of books and theatrical advertising (he's still baffled by the fact that he's worked on more than one hundred Broadway musicals and plays). However, nothing makes him happier than writing and illustrating stories for kids. He is the author/illustrator of the Spy Next Door series and the Pepper Party series from Scholastic Press, as well as the illustrator of *Food Trucks!*, *Delivery Trucks!*, and the Bots series from Simon & Schuster. He lives with his wife and children in Maplewood, New Jersey.

Christopher Mitten is originally from the cow-dappled expanse of southern Wisconsin, but he now spends his time roaming the misty wilds of suburban Chicago, drawing little people in little boxes.

Among others, Christopher has contributed work for Dark Horse, DC Comics, Oni Press, Vertigo, Image Comics, Marvel Comics, IDW, Black Mask, Gallery Books, Titan Comics, 44FLOOD, and Simon & Schuster.

Anoosha Syed is a Pakistani-Canadian illustrator and character designer for animation. She is the illustrator of APALA Honor Book *Bilal Cooks Daal* by Aisha Saeed, *I Am Perfectly Designed* by Karamo Brown and Jason Rachel Brown, and many more. Some of her past clients also include Google, Netflix, Dreamworks TV, and Disney Jr. In her spare time, Anoosha hosts a YouTube channel focusing on art education. Anoosha has a passion for creating charming characters with an emphasis on diversity and inclusion. She lives in Toronto with her husband.